Basic Maths Skills

Book 4

Helen Anderson

Adding to 100

46 + 23	55 + 32	64 + 34	21 + 48	73 + 24
41 + 34	23 + 55	16 + 42	34 + 25	61 + 36	52 + 43
26 + 52	43 + 46	76 + 12	13 + 52	68 + 31

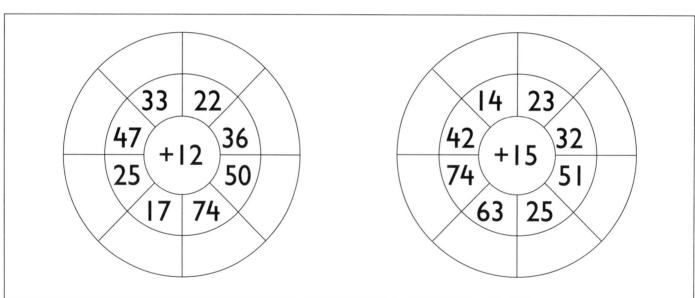

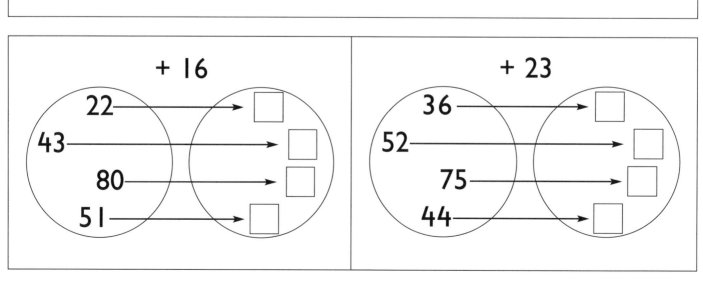

Taking away

46 − 23	59 − 12	38 − 17	96 − 82	32 − 11
75 − 42	87 − 33	48 − 26	89 − 25	98 − 62	76 − 21
63 − 33	57 − 13	34 − 14	99 − 52	85 − 42

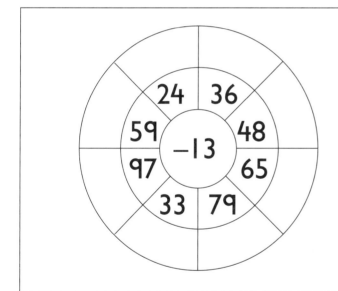

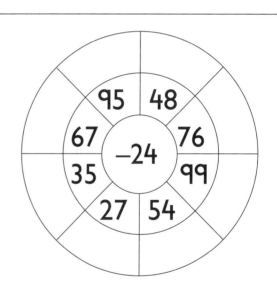

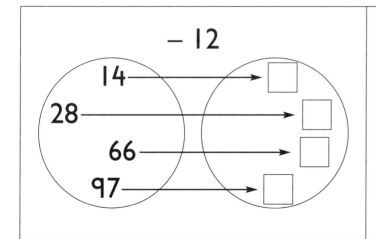

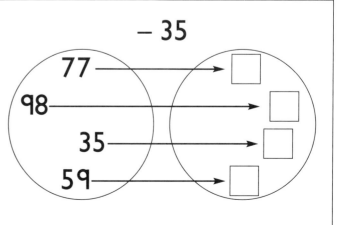

Adding and taking away

$18 + 10 + 21 = \boxed{}$ $37 + 10 + 12 = \boxed{}$

$36 + 20 + 12 = \boxed{}$ $44 + 20 + 15 = \boxed{}$

$55 + 31 + 13 = \boxed{}$ $22 + 43 + 31 = \boxed{}$

53	34	41	12	60	31	41
12	21	34	53	15	23	24
+ 24	+ 12	+ 23	+ 24	+ 12	+ 45	+ 33

62	41	20	12	23	33	16
24	22	15	25	30	23	60
+ 10	+ 33	+ 53	+ 42	+ 45	+ 43	+ 13

$12 + 15 - 3 = \boxed{}$ $14 + 15 - 4 = \boxed{}$

$16 + 13 - 2 = \boxed{}$ $32 + 22 - 20 = \boxed{}$

$24 + 25 - 15 = \boxed{}$ $45 + 34 - 19 = \boxed{}$

$60 + 31 - 20 = \boxed{}$ $50 + 50 - 40 = \boxed{}$

$25 + 33 - 18 = \boxed{}$ $41 + 58 - 36 = \boxed{}$

$16 + 43 - 22 = \boxed{}$ $32 + 64 - 50 = \boxed{}$

Count on in 3s

Colour the numbers.

1	2	3	4	5	6	7	8	9	10
11	12	13	14	15	16	17	18	19	20
21	22	23	24	25	26	27	28	29	30

Count on in 3s and write the numbers.

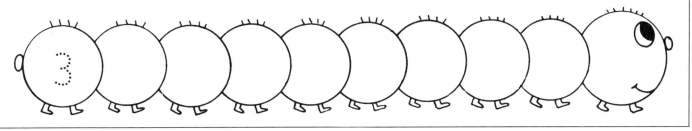

Complete the table wheel.

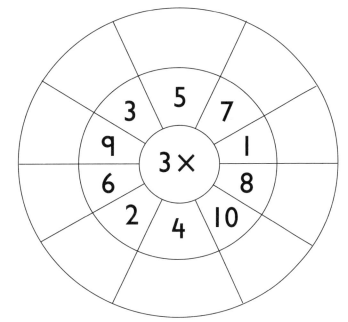

A quick check.

$3 \times 4 =$ ☐ $3 \times 8 =$ ☐ $3 \times 6 =$ ☐ $3 \times 2 =$ ☐

$3 \times 10 =$ ☐ $3 \times 5 =$ ☐ $3 \times 9 =$ ☐ $3 \times 7 =$ ☐

Sharing among 3

Share 3 balloons among 3 children.

☐ balloon each

3 ÷ 3 = ☐

Share 6 candles among 3 cakes.

☐ candle each

6 ÷ 3 = ☐

Share 9 eggs among 3 nests.

☐ eggs each

9 ÷ 3 = ☐

Share 12 fish among 3 nets.

☐ fish each

12 ÷ 3 = ☐

Share 15 cakes among 3 plates.

☐ cakes each

15 ÷ 3 = ☐

Sharing among 3

Share 18 carrots among 3 rabbits.

☐ carrots each

18 ÷ 3 = ☐

Share 21 sweets among 3 children.

☐ sweets each

21 ÷ 3 = ☐

Share 24 worms among 3 birds.

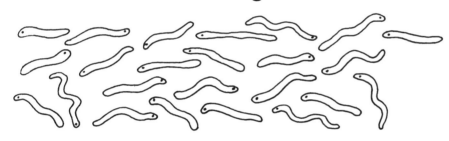

☐ worms each

24 ÷ 3 = ☐

Share 27 marbles among 3 children.

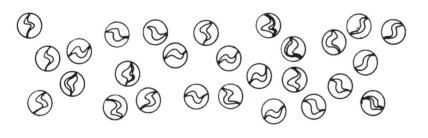

☐ marbles each

27 ÷ 3 = ☐

Share 30 acorns among 3 squirrels.

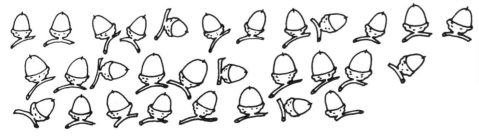

☐ acorns each

30 ÷ 3 = ☐

Dot to dot

Counting in 3s.

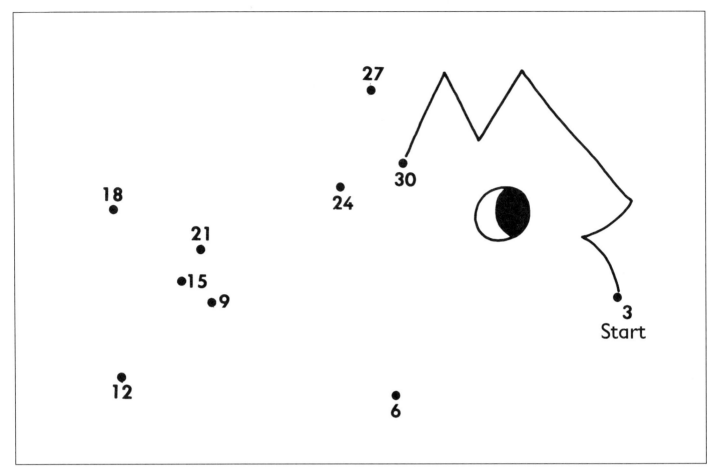

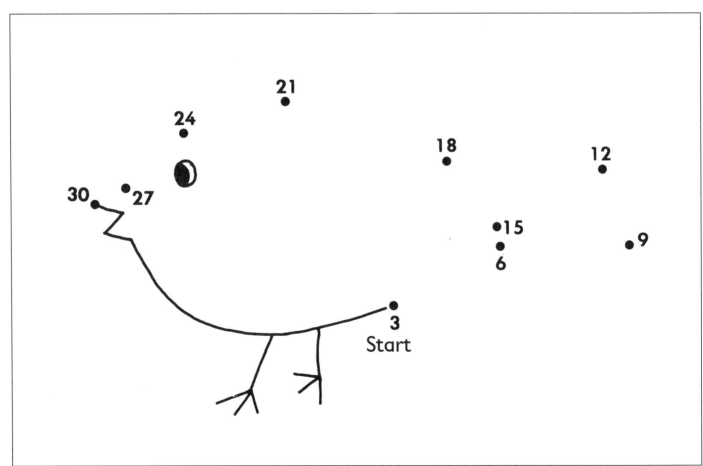

8

Count on in 4s

Colour the numbers.

1	2	3	4	5	6	7	8	9	10
11	12	13	14	15	16	17	18	19	20
21	22	23	24	25	26	27	28	29	30
31	32	33	34	35	36	37	38	39	40

Count on in 4s and write the numbers.

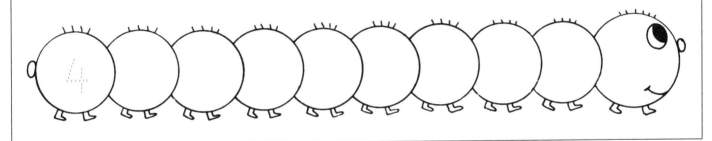

How many?

_____ legs   _____ legs   _____ legs   _____ legs

$4 \times 1 = \boxed{}$ $4 \times 2 = \boxed{}$ $4 \times 3 = \boxed{}$ $4 \times 4 = \boxed{}$

$5 \times 4 = \boxed{}$ $6 \times 4 = \boxed{}$ $7 \times 4 = \boxed{}$ $8 \times 4 = \boxed{}$

$9 \times 4 = \boxed{}$ $10 \times 4 = \boxed{}$

Sharing among 4

Share 4 lollies among 4 children.

□ lolly each

$4 \div 4 = $ □

Share 8 eggs among 4 nests.

□ eggs each

$8 \div 4 = $ □

Share 12 apples among 4 children.

□ apples each

$12 \div 4 = $ □

Share 16 carrots among 4 rabbits.

□ carrots each

$16 \div 4 = $ □

Share 20 loaves among 4 elephants.

□ loaves each

$20 \div 4 = $ □

Sharing among 4

Share 24 candles among 4 cakes.

☐ candles each

$24 \div 4 =$ ☐

Share 28 bananas among 4 monkeys.

☐ bananas each

$28 \div 4 =$ ☐

Share 32 worms among 4 birds.

☐ worms each

$32 \div 4 =$ ☐

Share 36 acorns among 4 squirrels.

☐ acorns each

$36 \div 4 =$ ☐

Share 40 sweets among 4 children.

☐ sweets each

$40 \div 4 =$ ☐

Dot to dot

Counting in 4s.
You will have to start three times to complete the picture.

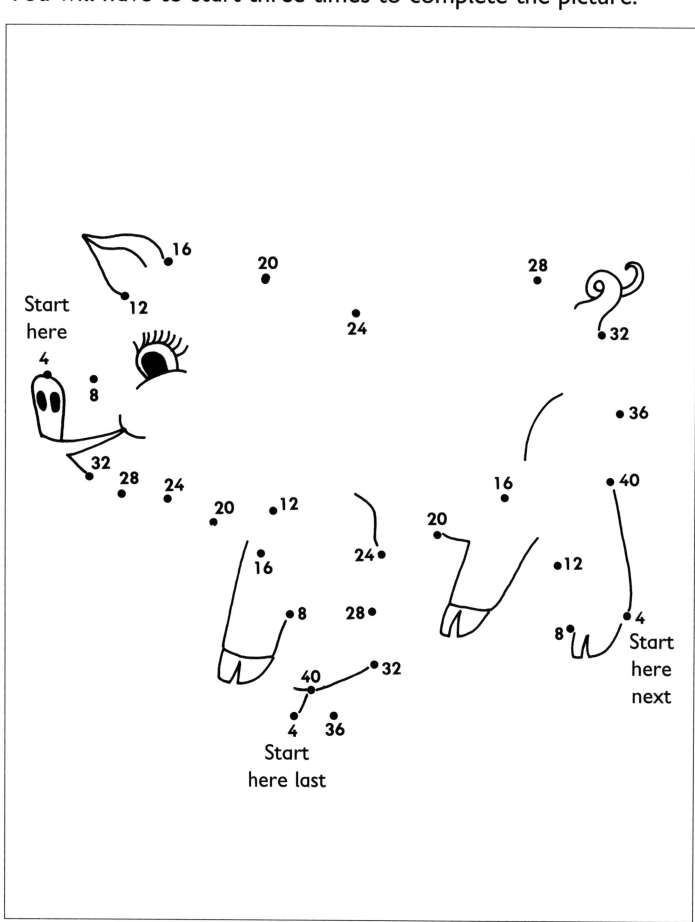

Adding and taking away

65 + 32	56 − 24	22 + 47	39 − 18	35 + 53
66 − 22	13 + 72	87 − 75	80 − 20	73 + 26	58 − 21
61 + 25	99 − 22	44 + 34	73 − 13	19 + 50

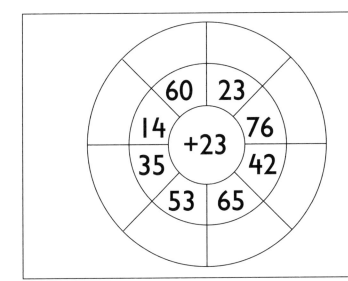

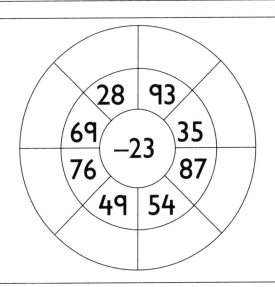

− 22

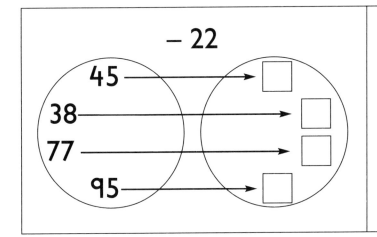

+ 35

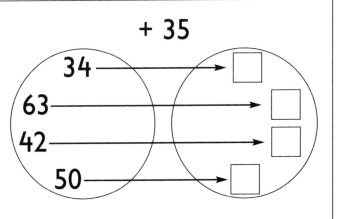

Practice blocks

$3 \times 2 =$ _____

$8 \div 2 =$ _____

$5 \times 2 =$ _____

$12 \div 2 =$ _____

$7 \times 2 =$ _____

$10 \times 2 =$ _____

$18 \div 2 =$ _____

$6 \times 2 =$ _____

$20 \div 2 =$ _____

$3 \times 3 =$ _____

$6 \div 2 =$ _____

$10 \times 3 =$ _____

$18 \div 3 =$ _____

$24 \div 3 =$ _____

$9 \times 3 =$ _____

$7 \times 3 =$ _____

$30 \div 3 =$ _____

$3 \times 8 =$ _____

$4 \times 2 =$ _____

$12 \div 4 =$ _____

$28 \div 4 =$ _____

$8 \times 4 =$ _____

$32 \div 4 =$ _____

$9 \times 4 =$ _____

$5 \times 4 =$ _____

$24 \div 4 =$ _____

$7 \times 4 =$ _____

$3 \times 2 =$ _____

$4 \times 3 =$ _____

$6 \times 4 =$ _____

$16 \div 2 =$ _____

$21 \div 3 =$ _____

$8 \times 2 =$ _____

$36 \div 4 =$ _____

$6 \times 3 =$ _____

$15 \div 3 =$ _____

Count on in 5s

Colour the numbers.

1	2	3	4	5	6	7	8	9	10
11	12	13	14	15	16	17	18	19	20
21	22	23	24	25	26	27	28	29	30
31	32	33	34	35	36	37	38	39	40
41	42	43	44	45	46	47	48	49	50

Count on in 5s and write the numbers.

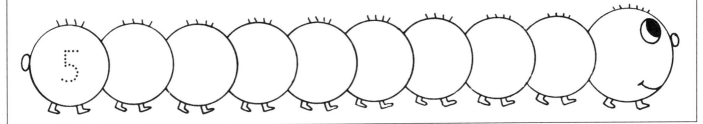

Complete the table wheel.

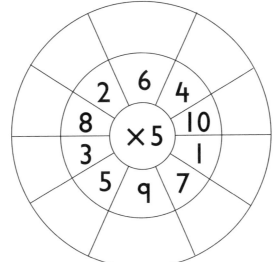

A quick check.

$5 \times 2 = \boxed{}$ $5 \times 6 = \boxed{}$ $5 \times 4 = \boxed{}$ $5 \times 10 = \boxed{}$

$5 \times 7 = \boxed{}$ $5 \times 3 = \boxed{}$ $5 \times 8 = \boxed{}$ $5 \times 5 = \boxed{}$

Sharing among 5

Share 5 bananas among 5 monkeys.

☐ banana each

$$5 \div 5 = \boxed{}$$

Share 10 fish among 5 tanks.

☐ fish each

$$10 \div 5 = \boxed{}$$

Share 15 apples among 5 children.

☐ apples each

$$15 \div 5 = \boxed{}$$

Share 20 eggs among 5 birds.

☐ eggs each

$$20 \div 5 = \boxed{}$$

Share 25 sweets among 5 children.

☐ sweets each

$$25 \div 5 = \boxed{}$$

Sharing among 5

Share 30 loaves among 5 elephants.

$\square$ loaves each

$30 \div 5 = \square$

Share 35 carrots among 5 rabbits.

$\square$ carrots each

$35 \div 5 = \square$

Share 40 marbles among 5 children.

$\square$ marbles each

$40 \div 5 = \square$

Share 45 acorns among 5 squirrels.

$\square$ acorns each

$45 \div 5 = \square$

Share 50 worms among 5 birds.

$\square$ worms each

$50 \div 5 = \square$

Dot to dot

Counting in 5s.

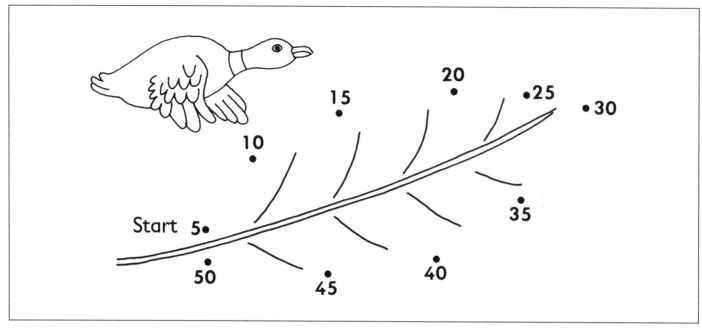

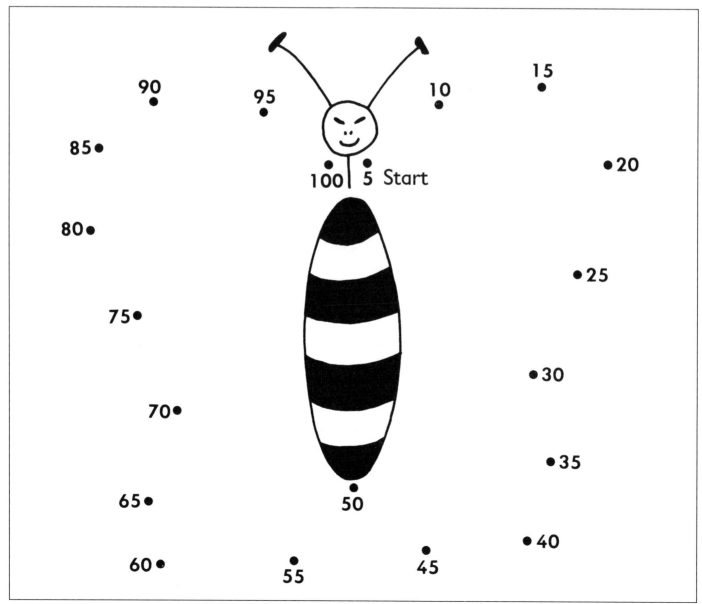

Colour the robot

Work out the answers to find the colours.
Use the colour code:

2 or 8 → red
3 or 10 → blue
4 or 12 → green
5 or 20 → orange
6 or 15 → yellow

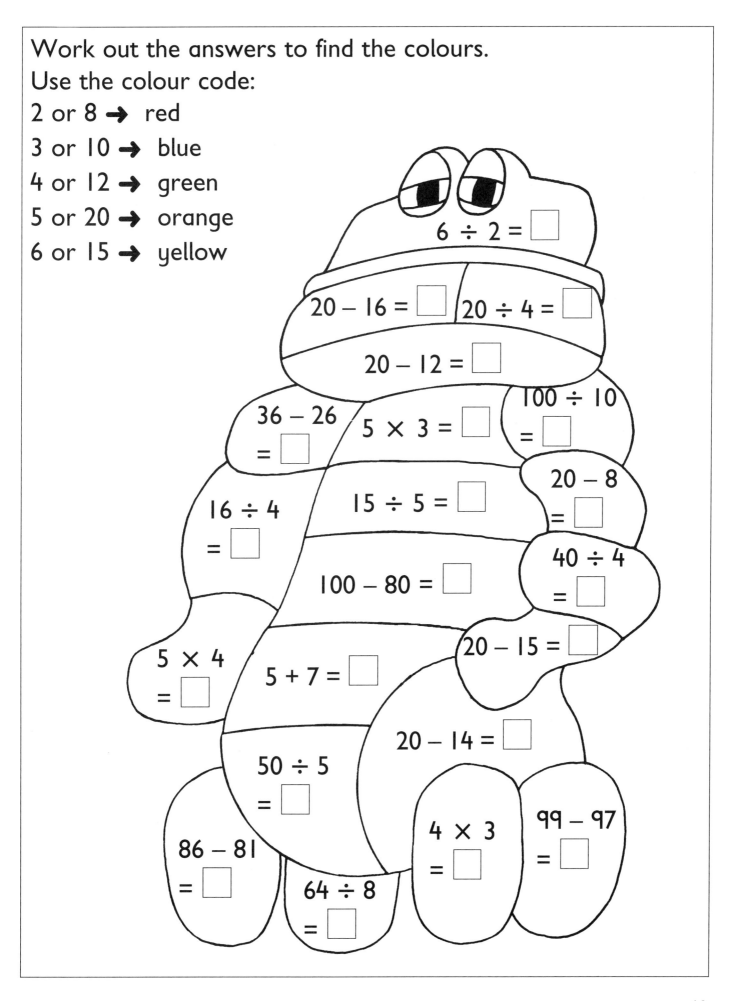

$6 \div 2 = \square$

$20 - 16 = \square$ $20 \div 4 = \square$

$20 - 12 = \square$

$36 - 26 = \square$ $5 \times 3 = \square$ $100 \div 10 = \square$

$16 \div 4 = \square$ $15 \div 5 = \square$ $20 - 8 = \square$

$100 - 80 = \square$ $40 \div 4 = \square$

$20 - 15 = \square$

$5 \times 4 = \square$ $5 + 7 = \square$

$20 - 14 = \square$

$50 \div 5 = \square$

$86 - 81 = \square$ $4 \times 3 = \square$ $99 - 97 = \square$

$64 \div 8 = \square$

Speed checks

18 + 10 _____

32 − 11 _____

5 × 2 _____

40 ÷ 5 _____

36 + 23 _____

59 − 34 _____

6 × 4 _____

36 ÷ 4 _____

Fifteen more than forty _____

Five times seven _____

Twelve less than
eighty-five _____

Share twenty-eight sweets
among four children.

_____ each

---

95 − 35 _____

8 × 2 _____

21 ÷ 3 _____

44 + 54 _____

9 × 3 _____

Twenty more than sixty _____

77 − 25 _____

30 ÷ 5 _____

Eleven less than
forty-two _____

8 × 4 _____

Eight times three _____

Share twenty-five sweets
among five children.

_____ each

---

18 ÷ 2 _____

7 × 4 _____

62 + 35 _____

99 − 53 _____

9 × 5 _____

18 ÷ 3 _____

Twenty-four add sixty _____

Four times nine _____

16 ÷ 4 _____

Seventy-eight
take away fifty _____

7 × 3 _____

Share twenty-four sweets
among three children.

_____ each

---

6 × 5 _____

20 ÷ 4 _____

45 + 54 _____

77 − 76 _____

14 ÷ 2 _____

7 × 5 _____

Share thirty-two sweets among
four children. _____ each

Seven times four _____

35 ÷ 5 _____

Add nineteen
to seventy _____

9 × 2 _____

35 ÷ 5 _____

Dot to dot

Counting in 10s.

You will have to start three times to complete the picture.

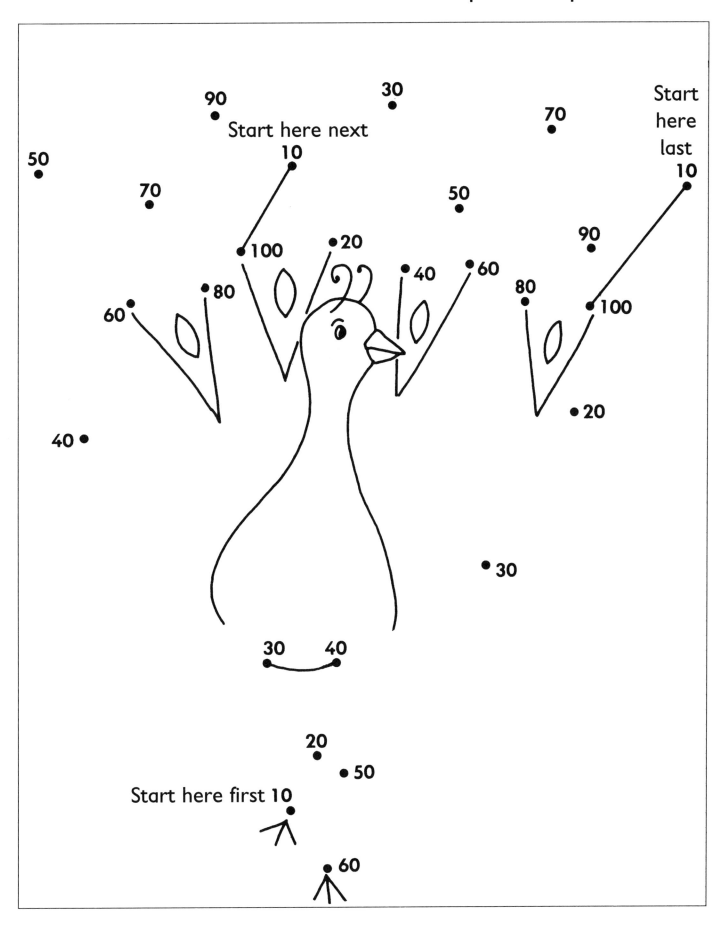

Which boat finishes first?

The boat with the lowest total is the winner. Colour it red.

Finish Line

1   18 − 6 = ☐   ÷ 3 = ☐   × 5 = ☐   − 13 = ☐

2   7 + 2 = ☐   × 3 = ☐   − 12 = ☐   ÷ 3 = ☐

3   6 + 10 = ☐   ÷ 2 = ☐   × 5 = ☐   − 30 = ☐

4   20 − 12 = ☐   × 3 = ☐   ÷ 4 = ☐   × 5 = ☐

What are the questions?

Do these calculations. Use the answers to find the correct letters from the code box below.

8×3 $86 - 44$ $30 \div 3$ $30 + 12$ $58 - 42$ 5×4

☐   ☐   ☐   ☐   ☐   ☐

☐☐☐   ☐☐☐

10×10 $40 \div 5$ $65 - 20$ 10×5 $54 - 12$ $28 \div 4$

☐   ☐   ☐   ☐   ☐   ☐

☐☐☐   ☐☐ ?

$100 - 90$ 6×4 $50 + 50$ $22 + 8 + 9$ 9×4 $24 \div 4$

☐   ☐   ☐   ☐   ☐   ☐

☐☐☐☐   ☐☐

$30 + 20$ $24 + 18$ $18 - 11$ $32 \div 4$ $7 + 3 + 8$ $70 + 30$ $20 - 11$ 9×5

☐   ☐   ☐   ☐   ☐   ☐   ☐   ☐

☐☐☐☐   ☐☐☐ ?

A	100	F	4	I	36	N	18	S	6	V	5
B	90	G	81	J	11	O	42	T	39	W	10
C	23	H	24	K	77	P	53	U	7	X	59
D	20			L	16	Q	19			Y	50
E	45			M	9	R	8			Z	96

Number design

Work out the calculations.

Find your answer in the colour code.

Colour the spaces:

2 or 8 ➔ red; 3 or 10 ➔ blue;

4 or 12 ➔ green; 5 or 20 ➔ orange; 6 or 15 ➔ yellow.

$100 - 98 = \square$

$30 \div 10 = \square$

$20 - 10 = \square$

$10 \div 5 = \square$

$40 \div 10 = \square$

$5 \times 3 = \square$

$76 - 72 = \square$

$4 \times 5 = \square$

$27 - 24 = \square$

$63 - 43 = \square$

$48 - 36 = \square$

$32 \div 4 = \square$

$80 - 78 = \square$

$20 \div 5 = \square$

$30 \div 3 = \square$

$100 - 95 = \square$

$50 \div 10 = \square$

$3 \times 4 = \square$

$75 - 60 = \square$

$1 + 2 + 3 + 4 + 2 = \square$

$7 + 8 = \square$

$24 \div 3 = \square$

$49 - 41 = \square$

$3 \times 5 = \square$

Practice blocks

$4 \times 4 =$ _____	$18 \div 2 =$ _____
$30 \div 3 =$ _____	$4 \times 6 =$ _____
$5 \times 6 =$ _____	$40 \div 5 =$ _____
$10 \times 4 =$ _____	$80 \div 10 =$ _____
$60 \div 10 =$ _____	$4 \times 9 =$ _____
$28 \div 4 =$ _____	$3 \times 7 =$ _____
$2 \times 10 =$ _____	$20 \div 4 =$ _____
$35 \div 5 =$ _____	$10 \times 8 =$ _____
$5 \times 8 =$ _____	$27 \div 3 =$ _____

$18 \div 3 =$ _____	$5 \times 9 =$ _____
$10 \times 7 =$ _____	$4 \times 8 =$ _____
$3 \times 9 =$ _____	$24 \div 3 =$ _____
$45 \div 5 =$ _____	$10 \times 10 =$ _____
$90 \div 10 =$ _____	$20 \div 2 =$ _____
$5 \times 7 =$ _____	$5 \times 5 =$ _____
$36 \div 4 =$ _____	$32 \div 4 =$ _____
$2 \times 8 =$ _____	$100 \div 10 =$ _____
$50 \div 5 =$ _____	$3 \times 8 =$ _____

Picture and word problems

There are ☐ bananas altogether.

There are ☐ monkeys.

Each monkey has ☐ bananas.

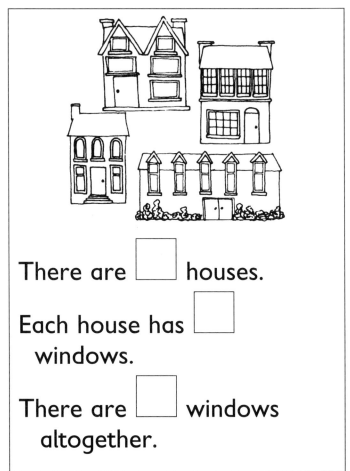

There are ☐ houses.

Each house has ☐ windows.

There are ☐ windows altogether.

Ann scores ☐

Ben scores ☐

Ann scores ☐ more than Ben.

There are ☐ plates.

There are ☐ cakes on each plate.

There are ☐ cakes altogether.

Picture and word problems

Amy had ☐ p in her purse.

She bought a pen for ☐ p.

Amy had ☐ p left.

For 2 children it costs ☐ p.

For 2 adults it costs ☐ p.

Altogether it costs ☐ p.

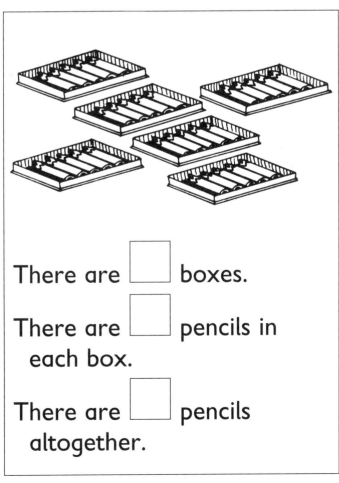

There are ☐ boxes.

There are ☐ pencils in each box.

There are ☐ pencils altogether.

There are ☐ acorns.

There are ☐ squirrels.

Each squirrel has ☐ acorns each.

Speed checks

28 + 30 _____

46 – 13 _____

5 × 4 _____

32 ÷ 4 _____

77 + 12 _____

90 – 20 _____

40 ÷ 5 _____

Sixty more than twenty _____

Four times four _____

Thirty-two less than sixty-six _____

Share twenty-five sweets equally among five children. _____ each

---

86 – 36 _____

9 × 2 _____

24 ÷ 3 _____

56 + 13 _____

10 × 5 _____

Sixteen more than fifty _____

4 × 9 _____

Twelve less than thirty-five _____

Eight times three _____

100 – 10 _____

Share eighty sweets equally among ten children. _____ each

---

5 × 7 _____

20 ÷ 2 _____

Add fifty to thirty-six _____

5 × 8 _____

From thirty-two take twelve _____

Eight times two _____

50 ÷ 5 _____

66 – 16 _____

2 × 8 _____

2 + 8 + 1 + 9 + 10 _____

Share twenty-seven acorns equally among three squirrels. _____

---

45 ÷ 5 _____

5 × 5 _____

96 – 45 _____

28 ÷ 4 _____

5 + 5 + 7 + 3 + 4 _____

100 – 20 _____

6 × 3 _____

Add seven, three, two and eight. _____

16 ÷ 2 _____

Share thirty-six worms equally among four birds. _____

3 × 7 _____

Cross-number puzzle

Clues

Across
1 7 + 8
2 5 × 5
4 18 × 2
5 50 + 25
6 24 ÷ 2
7 30 − 9
9 7 × 5
10 6 × 4
11 44 − 24
12 19 + 9
13 5 × 4
14 100 − 7

Down
1 20 − 5
2 3 × 7
3 8 × 2
4 40 − 8
5 50 + 21
6 Take 20 from 30
7 6 × 4
8 69 − 45
9 100 − 70
10 7 × 4
11 5 + 5 + 5 +5
12 30 − 7

Graphs

Paul and Ella visited Moss farm and saw:

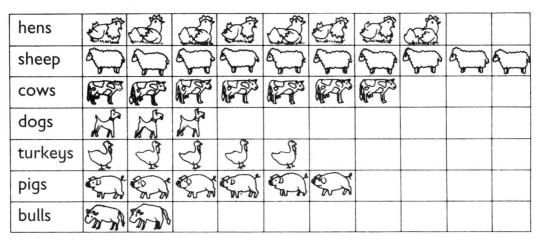

hens	🐔	🐔	🐔	🐔	🐔	🐔	🐔	🐔		
sheep	🐑	🐑	🐑	🐑	🐑	🐑	🐑	🐑	🐑	🐑
cows	🐄	🐄	🐄	🐄	🐄	🐄	🐄			
dogs	🐕	🐕	🐕							
turkeys	🦆	🦆	🦆	🦆	🦆					
pigs	🐖	🐖	🐖	🐖	🐖	🐖				
bulls	🐂	🐂								

1. How many sheep did they see? ☐ sheep

2. How many hens were there? ☐ hens

3. How many more sheep were there than hens? ☐ more sheep

4. How many cows and bulls did they count altogether? ☐ cows and bulls

5. How many pigs were there? ☐ pigs

6. How many turkeys did they see? ☐ turkeys

7. How many more pigs were there than turkeys? ☐ more pigs

8. How many dogs, pigs and sheep were there altogether? ☐ dogs, pigs and sheep

Crisps for Sale!

🍟				
🍟	🍟			🍟
🍟	🍟			🍟
🍟	🍟	🍟		🍟
🍟	🍟	🍟	🍟	🍟
🍟	🍟	🍟	🍟	🍟
🍟	🍟	🍟	🍟	🍟
🍟	🍟	🍟	🍟	🍟
Mon	Tues	Wed	Thurs	Fri

1. How many packets were sold on Tuesday? ☐ packets

2. On which day were 8 packets sold?.................................

3. On which day were the least number of packets sold?.................................

4. How many more packets were sold on Monday than Wednesday? ☐ more packets

5. How many crisps were sold altogether on Tuesday, Wednesday and Thursday ? ☐ packets

Final check

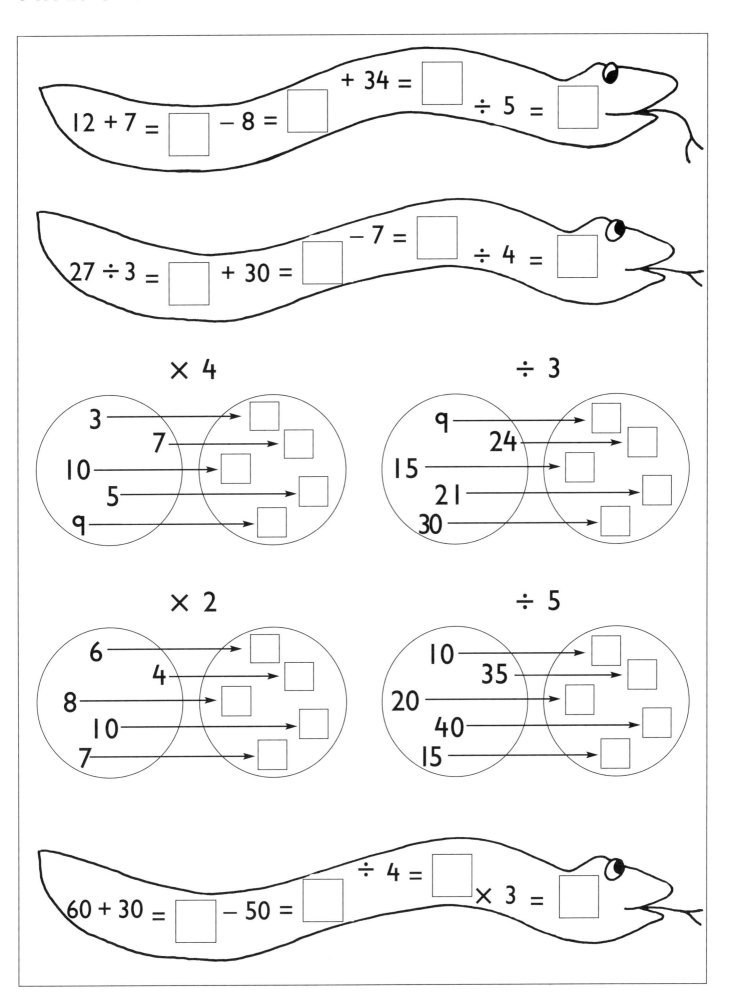

$12 + 7 =$ ☐ $- 8 =$ ☐ $+ 34 =$ ☐ $÷ 5 =$ ☐

$27 ÷ 3 =$ ☐ $+ 30 =$ ☐ $- 7 =$ ☐ $÷ 4 =$ ☐

$× 4$

3
7
10
5
9

$÷ 3$

9
24
15
21
30

$× 2$

6
4
8
10
7

$÷ 5$

10
35
20
40
15

$60 + 30 =$ ☐ $- 50 =$ ☐ $÷ 4 =$ ☐ $× 3 =$ ☐

This is to certify that

_____

has successfully completed

Basic Maths Skills
Book 4

Well done!